Spies in Spa[...]
Six Funny Plag[...]

by Stan Cullimore

Contents

Characters

Narrator
Rotor – the robot who is in charge.
Grumbles – a blue alien who likes to grumble.
Quiz – a red alien who likes to ask questions.
Greedy – an orange alien who likes to eat.
Smiler – a green alien who likes almost everything!

Longman

Edinburgh Gate
Harlow, Essex

Play One: *The Mission*

Narrator Far out in space, there was a small purple spaceship. It was travelling three times faster than light. Which is fast – very fast.

Quiz Rotor, how much longer is it going to take to get there?

(Rotor walks over to the control desk.)

Rotor According to my computers we will arrive in ... BEEP, BEEP, BEEP ... seven minutes' time.

Grumbles Seven minutes! Boring! Can't you get this rust bucket to go any faster, Rotor?

Narrator On board this spaceship there were four aliens and one robot.

(Greedy goes over to the food cupboard.)

Greedy I'm hungry.

Rotor Do not worry. We will soon arrive and then you will be able to eat your packed lunches.

Greedy I've already eaten them all! *(Burp)* And I'm still hungry.

Narrator They were spies from a distant planet.

Quiz What? You haven't eaten all four of the packed lunches have you?

Greedy Yes.

(Smiler wags an alien finger at Greedy.)

Smiler Oh, Greedy, you are a pain. You were only supposed to eat one of the packed lunches! The other three were for Grumbles, Quiz and me.

Greedy Sorry. *(Burp)* But I was just so hungry I couldn't stop myself.

Grumbles	Greedy isn't a "pain" at all. He's a great big greedy lump!
Narrator	In case you hadn't noticed by now, Grumbles is not a very polite alien.
Quiz	So, where are we going, Rotor?
Smiler	I don't care where we are going. All I know is that we'll have some fun! We always do when we go on a trip with Rotor.
Grumbles	You speak for yourself. If it was up to me, I would much rather be back home on Planet Plog rolling around in sticky treacle mud.
	(Grumbles gets onto the floor and starts rolling around.)
Rotor	We are going to a small, far away planet called … Earth.
Smiler	Earth – that sounds really interesting!
	(Grumbles stands up again.)
Grumbles	No, it doesn't. It sounds really boring. What a stupid name for a planet!
Greedy	I hope there's some nice food when we get to this "Earth" place. I'm hungry.

Grumbles	You're always hungry.
Rotor	I am afraid to say that we will not be landing on Earth. We will be staying in space and looking at it through our space scope.
Smiler	Fantastic! I love looking through the space scope.
Narrator	Two minutes later the space ship was very close to Earth. Rotor pushed a big red button marked, BRAKES. The spaceship began to slow down.
Quiz	Rotor! Why are we going to this "Earth" place, anyway?
Rotor	We are going there so that we can watch the Earthlings as they go about their daily lives …
	(Grumbles pulls a face.)
Grumbles	Ugh. That should be really interesting – I don't think!
Quiz	What is our mission, Rotor?
Rotor	Our mission is to find out exactly what sort of things Earthlings do. We also have to find out exactly why they do these things.

Quiz	You mean we're going to spy on them?
Rotor	Yes, that is correct.
Smiler	Spying! Great, I love spying. It's my favourite thing.
Greedy	You know, I don't think I've ever heard of these "Earthlings" before.
Quiz	What are they like, Rotor?
Rotor	Nobody knows much about them. We think they may be a race of foolish savages. Our mission is to find out if they show any signs of intelligence. We have five days to find out as much as we can. Then we must report back to Planet Plog.
Smiler	I think this trip could be fun. I only wish we could stay longer than five days.
Grumbles	I don't. I only wish you could shut up!
Rotor	We have now arrived at Earth.
	(The four aliens run to the window and look out.)
Narrator	Beneath them lay a small, blue planet.
Quiz	Is that it?
Greedy	It's tiny.
Smiler	I think it looks really exciting.
Grumbles	I think it looks really boring. I only hope these Earthlings aren't as boring as their planet.
Rotor	If you will all come and join me at the space scope we can begin to spy on the Earthlings.

Play Two: *Day One*

Five spies from the Planet Plog have been sent to Earth on board a small purple spaceship. Their mission? To watch the Earthlings through the space scope. To find out exactly what sort of things Earthlings do. To find out exactly just why they do these things …

Narrator   The four aliens left the window and went over to the space scope. Rotor pressed a button marked, CHAIRS. There was a soft humming sound. Four chairs rose up out of the floor.

(The four aliens sit down in the chairs.)

Rotor   When you are all sitting comfortably, we can begin.

Narrator   Rotor pressed some more buttons. Outside the spaceship the space scope began to move.

(Grumbles stands up, pulls a face and sits down again.)

Greedy   I can't sit comfortably on this chair. It's too hard!

Narrator   The space scope turned round until it was pointing at the small blue planet beneath them.

Rotor   You will see that the planet looks very small from up here.

Quiz   Why is it blue, Rotor?

Greedy   Is that because it's made out of blue cheese? I love blue cheese – and green cheese … and purple cheese … and brown cheese …

(Greedy starts to make slurping sounds.)

Grumbles   Do you ever stop thinking about food?

(Greedy thinks for a minute.)

Greedy   No, not really.

Smiler   Rotor, do you have any idea why the planet is called "Earth"? All the earth I've ever seen has been brown.

Rotor   That is true. "Earth" is a rather strange
               name for a blue planet.

               (Rotor blinks.)

Rotor   According to my computers … BEEP, BEEP, BEEP …
               Earthlings use the word "Earth" to mean dirt or soil.

Smiler   Wow. I suppose that means they have blue soil on "Earth".
               I've never seen that before.

               (Rotor blinks again.)

Greedy   I wish I hadn't thought of blue cheese. It's made me hungry
               again.

Rotor   According to my computers … BEEP, BEEP, BEEP … all
               that blue stuff we can see down there is, in fact, water.

Quiz   There is a lot of water on "Earth" isn't there?

Rotor   Yes. Two-thirds of the planet is covered in it.

Grumbles   So why don't they call the planet, "Water"? That would be a
               much better name than "Earth".

Rotor   I do not know why they chose that name.

Greedy   Perhaps it was a joke.

Rotor   I do not think so.

Grumbles   I think I know why they chose such a stupid name! They did it to show that they're a bunch of stupid fools! Now that is settled, can we go home?

Smiler   Come on, Grumbles, that's not a very nice thing to say, is it? The Earthlings can't help being stupid.

(Rotor pulls a lever.)

Narrator   The planet in the space scope seemed to leap upwards. The aliens all jumped in their chairs.

Grumbles   Careful, Rotor! You gave me a fright doing that.

Rotor   Sorry. I will try to move the space scope slowly from now on.

(Rotor slowly pulls on another lever.)

Narrator   Something came into view on the scope.

Quiz   What is that?

Smiler   I don't know. I've never seen anything like that before.

Rotor	That is the water which covers most of the planet. The Earthlings have a special word for it. They call it the "sea".
Narrator	The four aliens and the robot stared at the scope for a minute. Greedy was the first one to speak.
Greedy	I do wish it would stop going up and down like that. It's starting to make me feel sick.
	(Greedy makes horrible sick noises. Grumbles joins in.)
Grumbles	It's starting to make me feel sick as well. Rotor, can we look at something else for a change?
Narrator	Rotor moved the space scope until a sand-covered beach came into view.
Greedy	I don't know what all that yellow stuff is – but it's much better than all that blue stuff!
Rotor	I believe it is called, "sand". It is often found by "the seaside".
Smiler	Well I think it looks fantastic!
	(Grumbles points at the screen.)
Grumbles	Look! Did you see that? How disgusting! There are some horrible thin things moving across the sand. There, see them? They look like little blobs on sticks.
Greedy	Oh, no. Looking at them is worse than looking at the sea. I'm starting to feel sick again.
Quiz	What are those disgusting things, Rotor?
	(Quiz turns away from the screen in horror.)
Smiler	I must say – they do look a bit odd.
Rotor	Those things are "Earthlings".
Narrator	The aliens looked at one another.

Grumbles   Ugh! Do we have to spend the next few days looking at them?

Smiler   They're not all that bad. Look, one of the smaller ones is going into the blue stuff – the sea. This should be interesting.

Narrator   Rotor blinked.

Rotor   According to my computers … BEEP, BEEP, BEEP … a smaller Earthling is called a "child".

Quiz   Why is it going into the sea, Rotor?

Grumbles   Perhaps the bigger ones are making the child go into the sea because it has been naughty.

Greedy   What do you mean?

Grumbles   Well, looking at the sea made us feel sick. So being in the sea must be even worse!

Smiler   I think you're right. What a bunch of bullies. Making that poor little Earthling go into the sea!

Narrator	Rotor blinked.
Rotor	According to my computers … BEEP, BEEP, BEEP … the Earthlings like going into the sea – they think it is fun.
Quiz	What?
Smiler	They think that going into that disgusting blue stuff is fun?
Rotor	It is hard to understand.
Narrator	The aliens shook their heads.
Grumbles	I've said it before – and I'll say it again – these Earthlings are stupid!

Play Three: *Day Two*

Five spies from the Planet Plog have been sent to Earth on board a small purple spaceship. Their mission? To watch the Earthlings through the space scope. To find out exactly what sort of things Earthlings do. To find out exactly just why they do these things …

Narrator	The four aliens and the robot called Rotor were sitting in chairs, watching the space scope in front of them. On the screen they could see a sand-covered beach. There were several "Earthlings" sitting on the beach.
	(Quiz leans forward to stare at the screen.)
Quiz	Now what are they doing?
	(Rotor pulls a lever.)
Narrator	The sand-covered beach in the space scope leapt into focus. The aliens all jumped in their chairs.
Grumbles	I do wish you wouldn't keep on doing that, Rotor!
Greedy	It makes it look as if the Earthlings are coming straight at us!
	(The aliens all shudder.)
Grumbles	What a horrible thought.
Smiler	Please don't do it again, Rotor.
Rotor	I am sorry for any distress I have caused you. I will attempt to be more careful in future.
Greedy	Hey, Rotor, is there anything to eat on Earth? I'm starving.
Smiler	You're always starving.
Grumbles	And you're always going on about it.
Greedy	I was only asking.
Quiz	Come on, Rotor, what shall we look at next?
	(Rotor slowly pulls on another lever.)

Narrator	A smaller Earthling – a "child" – could now be seen splashing about in the waves.
Quiz	What is that child doing?
Smiler	I haven't got a clue. I've never seen a creature do anything like that before.
Grumbles	I knew it.
Quiz	What?
Grumbles	These Earthlings are crazy.
	(Greedy starts making slurping noises.)
Greedy	I wonder what Earthlings would taste like? They might be quite nice if they were cooked properly.
	(Smiler sighs.)
Smiler	You can't eat them, Greedy. That would be extremely rude. It's bad manners to eat people after you've spied on them!
Greedy	I was only wondering.
Grumbles	That small Earthling splashing about in the sea has covered itself in water.
Quiz	What do you think it is doing, Rotor?
Rotor	I do not know.

14

Smiler	Perhaps the Earthlings need to keep themselves wet so that they do not dry up in the heat of the sun.
	(Rotor points at the screen.)
Rotor	I think that maybe you are right, Smiler. That pink stuff they're wearing does not look as if it is much use.
Smiler	The light from their sun would dry it up in no time.
Narrator	Rotor blinked. Computers in the robot's brain whirred into life. Lights flashed.
Rotor	According to my computers, that pink stuff is called … BEEP, BEEP, BEEP … "skin".
Grumbles	I've just noticed something. Not all the Earthlings are wearing pink stuff. There are lots of different colours.
Rotor	That is because "skin" comes in all sorts of different shades and colours. They include: brown, pink, black, white and yellow.
	(Greedy makes more slurping noises.)
Greedy	Just like sweets. I bet all the different colours have their own flavour.
Narrator	The slurping got louder.
Greedy	That does it – I've got to eat some of them now!
Rotor	You are wrong there, Greedy. According to my computers … BEEP, BEEP, BEEP … beneath their skin all Earthlings are exactly the same.
Smiler	And I've told you before, Greedy. You are NOT going to eat any of the Earthlings.
Greedy	Oooh! That's not fair.
Smiler	Look! The little Earthling has just got out of the water and is rubbing itself dry with a big white fluffy thing.
Greedy	Mmm! That sounds even better. Dried Earthling. I could just nibble on one of those right now.

Rotor	According to my computers, the big white fluffy thing is called a … BEEP, BEEP, BEEP … "towel".
Quiz	What do you think it is going to do now, Rotor?
	(Rotor shrugs.)
Rotor	I do not have the faintest idea.
Narrator	The four aliens watched as the small Earthling lay the big white fluffy towel down on the sand.
Quiz	Does anyone know what it is doing?
	(The other three aliens and Rotor shake their heads.)
Narrator	The child lay down on the towel and stretched out in the sun.
Rotor	It seems to be lying down in the sunshine. It will get very hot if it is not careful.
Smiler	Perhaps it wants to get hot.
Greedy	Yes. Perhaps it is cooking itself. How very thoughtful!
Grumbles	Even Earthlings aren't stupid enough to cook themselves – are they?
Smiler	I don't know about that. Look!
Narrator	A larger Earthling came over and handed the child something soft on a stick.

Quiz	What is that?
Rotor	According to my calculations, that soft thing on a stick is a very cold substance called "ice cream".
Smiler	That's clever. I expect the Earthling will rub the ice cream all over its skin to keep it cool.
Greedy	Just my luck!
Quiz	What's wrong with that?
Greedy	If that stuff is cold it is bound to taste disgusting!
Quiz	That is true.
Smiler	Oh no, I don't believe it …
Greedy	That's disgusting!
Narrator	The aliens looked on in horror as the Earthling slowly began to eat the cold stuff.
	(All four aliens turn away from the space scope and shudder.)
Grumbles	I've said it before and I'll say it again. These Earthlings are stupid!
Narrator	The other aliens looked at one another.
Rotor	I must say – I am starting to agree with Grumbles.

Play Four: *Day Three*

Five spies from the Planet Plog have been sent to Earth on board a small purple spaceship. Their mission? To watch the Earthlings through the space scope. To find out exactly what sort of things Earthlings do. To find out exactly just why they do these strange things ...

Narrator	On the third day of their mission the four aliens and the robot (called Rotor) were sitting in chairs, staring at the space scope in front of them. Suddenly the screen went blank.
	(The four aliens groan.)
Quiz	What's going on now, Rotor?
Grumbles	I expect the sight of all these disgusting Earthlings has broken the space scope.
Smiler	I must say, I'm not surprised. They do look a bit sick.
Greedy	I expect Earthlings would look a lot better if they were cooked properly and put on a plate.
Rotor	Do not worry. Normal service will be resumed as soon as possible.
	(Rotor flicks a switch.)
Narrator	The space scope screen flickered back into life.
Quiz	Come on, Rotor. Can't you find us anything interesting to look at?
	(Rotor slowly pulls on a lever.)
Narrator	Beneath the spaceship the space scope twisted round as it searched for a new target.
Quiz	What is that strange square thing down there?
Smiler	It looks like some sort of building for Earthlings.
Grumbles	There's lots of space around the outside – and the ground has got all sorts of patterns on it.

Quiz	What is it, Rotor?
Narrator	Rotor looked thoughtful – or rather – as thoughtful as any metal robot can look. Computer noises filled the air.
Rotor	According to my onboard computers … BEEP, BEEP, BEEP … that building is used for the purpose of keeping smaller Earthlings locked up during the day. It is called a "school".
	(The aliens look at one another and shudder.)
Quiz	So a "school" is a sort of place for punishing children, is it?
Smiler	That doesn't sound very nice.
Grumbles	These Earthling children must be very badly behaved if they have to be locked up all day long.
Rotor	The space around the school that has got all sorts of patterns on it is called a "playground".
Quiz	What is the playground used for, Rotor?
Grumbles	Knowing the Earthlings, I expect it is something really horrible.
Rotor	The children are made to run around it in circles. Like this!
	(Rotor runs around in circles – the way children do when they are playing chase.)
Quiz	What for?
	(Rotor shrugs.)
Rotor	I do not know. But it seems that they spend their time shouting out to each other and getting excited.

Smiler   I'm not surprised. I expect they're trying to escape!

Greedy   I don't like the sound of all this running around.

Grumbles   Nor do I.

Smiler   I think this school place sounds horrible. Earthling children don't deserve to be treated like that – even if they do look a bit sick.

(Greedy looks worried.)

Greedy   I quite agree. Apart from anything else, all that running must ruin their flavour.

Grumbles   If you ask me, I think these Earthlings are crazy.

Quiz   What happens to the children when they get back inside the school, Rotor?

Rotor   I do not know exactly. But my computers tell me … BEEP, BEEP, BEEP … that they are forced to sit on chairs and listen to bigger Earthlings called "teachers". These "teachers" like to go on and on about various things.

Quiz   What sort of things?

Rotor   I believe that these teachers spend a lot of time reading words out of books.

Smiler   Well, I find that most odd.

Quiz	Why?
Smiler	Well, if Earthlings have got books they can't be all that stupid.
Grumbles	That's true!
Narrator	Rotor blinked. Computers in the robot's brain whirred back into life. Lights flashed.
Rotor	According to my computers … BEEP, BEEP, BEEP … these bigger Earthlings also spend a lot of time teaching the children how to do things called "sums".
Grumbles	"Sums" – that's a funny word.
Quiz	What exactly are "sums", Rotor?
Greedy	Can you eat them?
Rotor	No, you cannot eat them. From what I can make out they appear to be some sort of mental torture.
	(The aliens all look at one another – shocked.)
Quiz	What does that mean?
Grumbles	Whatever it means – "sums" don't sound very nice to me!
Greedy	If you ask me, I think the small Earthlings would actually like me to eat them.
Smiler	Why do you think that, Greedy?
Greedy	Well if I ate them they wouldn't have to run around the playground …
Quiz	That is true!
Greedy	… they wouldn't have to get locked up in a school …
Smiler	Which can't be much fun!
Greedy	… and most important of all, they wouldn't have to be tortured by the teachers – with sums!
	(The other aliens all look at one another.)
Narrator	No one spoke for a while. At last Smiler said …

Smiler	Well, when you put it like that …
Quiz	It does make rather a lot of sense!
Grumbles	I know I've said this before – but I really do think it's worth saying again …
Rotor	I know, I know. These Earthlings are stupid!
Smiler	I think they're worse than that. I think they are just plain crazy!
	(Greedy looks hopeful.)
Grumbles	So, does that mean I can eat some of them?
Smiler	No, it does not!
	(Greedy looks sad.)
Grumbles	Oooh, that's not fair.
Quiz	Can we look at something else now, please, Rotor?
Grumbles	Yeah. I'm bored with looking at this school.
Smiler	Very well.
	(Rotor leans forward and begins to fiddle with the space scope.)
Narrator	The screen fuzzed over. The aliens sighed.
Grumbles	That's better!

Play Five: *Day Four*

Five spies from the Planet Plog have been sent to Earth on board a small purple spaceship. Their mission? To watch the Earthlings through the space scope. To find out exactly what sort of things Earthlings do. To find out exactly just why they do these strange things ...

Narrator	On the fourth day of their mission the four aliens and the robot, Rotor, were sitting in chairs staring at the blank space scope in front of them.
	(Grumbles gets up and starts to walk around the deck.)
Grumbles	This really is so boring.
Smiler	Come on, Rotor. Do something.
Narrator	Rotor did not reply. The robot was busy at the controls of the space scope.
Quiz	What are you doing now, Rotor?
Rotor	I am trying to find something of interest for us to observe.
	(Rotor flicks a couple of switches.)
Narrator	Beneath the spaceship the space scope twisted round as it searched for a new and interesting target.
Quiz	I've just had an idea! Rotor, can you try and find us a place where Earthlings go to have fun?
Smiler	What a great idea, Quiz. I would love to see where the Earthlings go to enjoy themselves.
Grumbles	I don't believe they ever do actually enjoy themselves. They're too busy being stupid all the time.
Narrator	The space scope screen flickered back into life.
Greedy	If I don't eat something soon I'm going to starve.
Grumbles	If ever an alien could do with starving for a while – it's YOU, you greedy lump!
Greedy	I am not greedy! *(Burp)* I've just got a big appetite!

Rotor   There we are. Now that looks interesting.

            (The aliens all look at the space scope screen.)

Narrator   The aliens frowned.

Quiz   What is it supposed to be?

Greedy   I don't know. All I know is that it doesn't look very edible to me!

Smiler   I think it looks like some sort of "school" building with funny coloured lights flashing on and off inside it.

Quiz   Do you know what it is, Rotor?

            (Grumbles sits down.)

Grumbles   Don't tell me – I'll take a guess. It's yet another place where the Earthlings get up to all sorts of weird stuff!

Rotor   I do not understand what happens inside this building.

Quiz   What do you mean?

Rotor   I mean that what happens makes no sense to me. All I know is that it is a place where the smaller Earthlings go to relax and meet their friends.

Quiz   What happens when the Earthlings get inside, Rotor?

Rotor   If you will all be patient for a moment I shall focus the space scope so that we can observe the inside of the building.

            (Rotor fiddles with the control panel.)

Narrator	The space scope leapt into focus – showing the scene inside the building.
Grumbles	Now that is weird!
Quiz	What is going on?
Narrator	The aliens were looking at a school hall. At one end there was a stage set up. The funny coloured flashing lights were pointing at a large group of children standing in the middle of the room.
Rotor	According to the information I have stored in my memory banks … BEEP, BEEP, BEEP … we are watching something that is called a "school disco".
Greedy	So this is what Earthlings do to enjoy themselves – they stand around looking stupid. That makes sense!
Quiz	Is this all they ever do at a "school disco", Rotor?
Rotor	I do not think so. It appears that they have come here to have a "dance".
Smiler	I've never heard of that before.
Quiz	What is it?
	(Rotor blinks several times.)
Rotor	My computers lead me to believe that … BEEP, BEEP, BEEP … "dancing" involves Earthlings throwing themselves around the room in time to music.
Grumbles	You see – I told you they would get up to something weird in there! They always do!

Quiz	But why do they do it?
Smiler	Perhaps they do it so that the other Earthlings have got something to laugh at.
Grumbles	Now that would make sense!
	(Rotor blinks again.)
Narrator	Computers in the robot's brain whirred back into life. Lights flashed.
Rotor	According to my computers … BEEP, BEEP, BEEP … this "dancing" is not supposed to be amusing. It is supposed to look "cool".
	(Quiz looks puzzled.)
Quiz	What's "cool"?
	(Greedy looks hopeful.)
Greedy	Do you mean – like a long, cool refreshing drink?
Rotor	No. According to the Earthlings, "cool" means good, impressive or fashionable.
	(The aliens all nod happily.)
Smiler	Well, that sounds interesting.
Grumbles	Yeah! At last we've found something worth watching.
Quiz	When will they start this "cool dancing" then, Rotor?
Rotor	I believe it happens when the music starts.
Greedy	Can I just say something?
Smiler	Not if it involves eating Earthlings.
Greedy	Oh, in that case I'll keep quiet.
Narrator	In the school hall, the DJ began to put on a track from his favourite CD. Music filled the air. The aliens groaned in horror.
Quiz	Aaargh! What is that terrible noise, Rotor?

Rotor	That awful sound is Earthling music. I shall turn it down so that it does not damage your delicate hearing organs.
	(Rotor turns the music down.)
Narrator	The children in the school hall began to dance. The aliens watched in stunned silence for a few moments.
Quiz	So that's supposed to be good, impressive and fashionable, is it?
Rotor	Yes.
Grumbles	I know I've probably said this before …
Smiler	Just about a million times.
Grumbles	… but these Earthling are …
Quiz	Crazy?
Smiler	Mad?
Rotor	Extremely foolish?
Greedy	Not worth eating?
Grumbles	All of those things. But most of all they are STUPID!

Play Six: *Day Five*

Five spies from the Planet Plog have been sent to Earth on board a small purple spaceship. Their mission? To watch the Earthlings through the space scope. To find out exactly what sort of things Earthlings do. To find out exactly just why they do these strange things ...

Narrator	On the fifth and final day of their mission the four aliens and the robot, Rotor, were sitting in chairs staring at the blank space scope screen in front of them.
Grumbles	Here we go again – about to waste yet another day watching these primitive Earthlings.
Greedy	And not even eating a single one of them! I think it's a crying shame.
Quiz	Why?
	(Greedy sighs.)
Greedy	Well, now we'll never know what they taste like!
Smiler	I tell you something. When we first came here I thought this mission was going to be great fun. But now I can't wait to go home.
Grumbles	Nor can I. These Earthlings are nothing but a race of brain-dead, boring idiots!
Rotor	They certainly are extremely backward!
Grumbles	When I get back to the Planet Plog the first thing I'm going to do is to throw myself into the deepest puddle of sticky treacle mud I can find.
Smiler	I think I'll join you!
Quiz	So will I!
Rotor	I would do the same – but I think that the treacle mud would damage my circuits.
	(Greedy looks over at the empty food cupboard and sighs.)

Greedy	I'm not sure I'll ever get home – I think I might starve on the way.
Quiz	So, what shall we look at today, Rotor?
Rotor	I don't know. I shall set the space scope to RANDOM. We will just have to wait and see what exciting new phenomenon it finds for us to observe.
	(Rotor presses a button on the control panel of the space scope.)
Narrator	Beneath the spaceship the space scope whizzed round in search of a new and exciting target.
Grumbles	Whatever it is, it's bound to be weird! Everything else we've looked at on Earth has been, well, weird!
Narrator	The space scope screen flickered into life.
	(The aliens frown at the screen in front of them.)
Quiz	Now what is that supposed to be?
Rotor	It appears to be some sort of green area surrounded by thousands of seats.
	(Smiler points.)
Smiler	Look! There are some white lines painted on the green stuff.
	(Quiz turns to Rotor.)

Quiz	What do you think they are for, Rotor?
Grumbles	Don't tell me – I'll take a guess. It looks like some sort of playground. Yet another place where Earthlings force their children to run around and get excited!
Rotor	Actually, you are almost right, Grumbles. Except it is not children who run around and get excited this time. It is the grown-up Earthlings.
Quiz	Why do they do that, then?
	(Rotor blinks.)
Rotor	I do not fully understand why. But according to the information I have stored in my memory banks … BEEP, BEEP, BEEP … we are looking at something that is called a "football pitch".
Quiz	Do you have any idea what the Earthlings use it for?
Rotor	Yes. They use it as a place to do something that is called "football".
Smiler	I've never heard of that before.
Quiz	Nor have I. What is it?
	(Rotor blinks again.)
Rotor	My computers lead me to believe that … BEEP, BEEP, BEEP … "football" is some sort of game.
	(Smiler nods wisely.)
Smiler	I see. I presume the name "football" must refer to the shape of an Earthling's feet.
Grumbles	No way – that would be far too sensible for Earthlings.
Quiz	What do you mean, Smiler?
Smiler	Well, if the game is called "football", that must mean that an Earthling's foot is shaped like a ball.
Grumbles	But that's not true. Earthlings' feet are long and stick shaped – just like the rest of their disgusting and puny bodies.

Rotor   That is entirely correct.

(Greedy puts up a hand.)

Greedy   Can I just say something at this point?

Quiz   What?

(Greedy puts the hand down again.)

Greedy   Is it time to go home yet? *(Burp)* Only I'm starving.

Quiz   Have you got any idea as to how they play this game of theirs, Rotor?

(Rotor blinks.)

Narrator   Computers in the robot's brain whirred into life. Lights flashed.

Rotor   According to my computers … BEEP, BEEP, BEEP … 22 Earthlings play in each game. The idea is that they should run around the green area – inside the white lines – whilst at the same time trying to kick a small circular object into a net.

Quiz   Where's the fun in that?

Smiler	I must say, it does sound rather easy.
Rotor	It's not that easy. There is only one ball between the 22 of them.
	(The aliens all shrug.)
Smiler	So what? They could easily line up and take it in turns to kick the ball into the net. Simple.
Grumbles	Yeah! Even Earthlings could manage to do that.
Smiler	Doesn't sound much of a game to me.
	(Rotor looks doubtful.)
Rotor	Hmm. I believe that lining up and taking it in turns to kick the ball into the net is against the rules.
Grumbles	Typical! The Earthlings come up with an easy game and then they make up a load of rules to make it harder to play.
	(The aliens look at each other and sigh.)
Quiz	Do you think we're ready to make our report on Earthlings yet, Rotor?
Rotor	Yes, I do. It is now obvious to me that these Earthlings are an entirely unintelligent species …
Grumbles	I could have told you that days ago!
Greedy	And definitely NOT worth eating.
Rotor	… now let us return to our own Planet.
Smiler	And fast!
Narrator	With that, Rotor pressed a button and the small purple spaceship set sail – never to return!